# Making very difficult things easy to do

A self-help guide to greatness written
by the world's highest achieving dog (Bobs)

*Handwritten inscription:* HOPE YOU
ENJOY IT
TERUJA.
REGARDS,
JONAtHAN

## Jonathan
## Cross

Illustrated by Royston Robertson

The Book Guild Ltd

First published in Great Britain in 2022 by
The Book Guild Ltd
Unit E2 Airfield Business Park,
Harrison Road, Market Harborough,
Leicestershire. LE16 7UL
Tel: 0116 2792299
www.bookguild.co.uk
Email: info@bookguild.co.uk
Twitter: @bookguild

Typeset in 11pt Minion Pro

Printed and bound by CPI Group (UK) Ltd, Croydon, CR0 4YY


ISBN 978 1914471 681


British Library Cataloguing in Publication Data.
A catalogue record for this book is available from the British Library.

Please visit the author website jcrossauthor.com and follow on Twitter: @dog_bobs

Thank you to my family and friends.

# ONE

Walk a mile in my shoes,
if I had shoes

The first step on the
footpath to greatness

## Don't over-complicate the things that aren't over-complicated

It's possible to achieve the impossible. Just cross out 'im' at the start of the word. That's what I do, and I do it every day. Well, most days. Some days, I just sleep, or steal socks. We all need a bit of downtime every now and then.

I remember when I was a pup, someone once asked me, 'how do you make the unachievable, achievable, Bobs?' I told them, 'it's all about getting rid of the 'un'.' They said, 'that's unbelievable'. I said, 'no, believable'.

I've been burying the 'im' and 'un' words of this world for a long time now. So much so, I don't know where they are anymore. I've looked for them but can't find them, no matter how much I dig. I just end up with a muddy nose and muddy paws, with my front paws slightly muddier than my back paws. I find if I hop back into the house, I don't get everywhere quite as muddy as on all four paws though.

Anyway, how do we become great at everything we do? It's easy. Just do what I do. As someone once said, 'some are born great, some achieve greatness, and others have to read self-help guides written by high-achieving dogs'. You're probably in the latter category.

For this self-help book, I'll be your guide dog on the footpath to greatness, even though I've had no training and don't have any reflective gear.

So, find a patch of sunlight, read on, understand, learn, apply, copy the useful ideas and ignore the ones where it might look like I've lost the plot (I haven't, I know where the plot is, although sometimes it has ended up under the sofa), and let the self-help improvement journey begin…

## There are biscuits in the cupboard – you just need to open the door

Born in a litter of ten, it was obvious from a young age that I was destined for greatness. First to open my eyes, first to bark, first to do my business in the garden to earn a treat when you came back into the house. I've earnt a lot of treats since then.

It was a long journey for me from the puppy playpen to Hollywood, space travel, and leading the United Nations and achieving world peace. Well, world peace for a bit. Then everyone started arguing again. I can't help that. We need to train world leaders better, give them a treat when they stop fighting. Reward good behaviour. You too should reward your own good behaviour. When you do a good thing, have a drink and a biscuit. If no-one's looking have another biscuit. Biscuits are brilliant.

It was actually my time in Hollywood that showed me the power of biscuits. I was appearing in a film, it was a blockbuster film about space or something, it might have had Tom Hanks in it, I can't remember. Most films seem to have Tom Hanks in them. Maybe it wasn't about space, it might just have been about dogs. Or maybe sharks.

Anyway, I had to say this line, 'before I save the world, could I have a biscuit?' And for that, they gave me an Oscar. An Oscar is a sort of golden bone trophy that's good for burying.

It's good to win awards. They show everyone else that you're better than them. Then they want to win one. But they can't because they're not as good. They could try a bit more in future years but they might never be good enough. With this self-help guide, you'll soon be winning lots of awards. You won't know where they're all coming from. They'll just be on the doorstep with the milk.

## If others don't recognise
## your greatness, bark louder

I've got lots of awards and lots of certificates. I keep them in the bottom drawer in the kitchen, along with my chews, pull toys and towels for when I come in from the garden all muddy again. Quite a few of the certificates are in frames; that shows they're more important than the ones that are in the cardboard folder. The certificates in the cardboard folder are mainly ones that I've won for things like swimming and paint-a-pot. The certificates in the picture frames are the most impressive ones – Olympics, Nobel Peace Prize, Dog Most Likely to Have Won Crufts Had They Let Me In, that sort of thing, high-level stuff.

The two Yappy Dogs from across the road say nasty things about the framed certificates. That's because they're just jealous. They say the certificates have either been badly drawn in pencil or are just photos of some of my favourite sticks. They're wrong. They're so wrong. There's no way I'd go round the garden taking photos of my favourite sticks, particularly the ones from the big trees at the end of the garden that are nice and bendy and good for chewing, printing them off on the home printer and then placing them in some picture frames that you might be able to find possibly in the understairs cupboard. Those Yappy Dogs don't have a clue. But they do have a reputation.

The Yappy Dogs

## Close your ears to cynics and the noise of fireworks

I think you probably need to know a bit more about the Yappy Dogs. This will be useful to you for a couple of reasons. One – learning from their mistakes will help you on your journey to becoming a bit more great, and, two – you'll know to cross the road so they don't try to snap at you. They're like that. I've seen people smile at the two old ladies who walk with the Yappy Dogs but that smile is a mask for fear, hatred and ridicule. Not long after they've walked past the Yappy Dogs, people say things like, 'I normally time my walk to avoid them but I was late out today,' or, 'I hope they don't get lost on the way back from their morning walk,' although I'm not sure whether that last comment is caring or not.

The Yappy Dogs seem like they've been on the street forever. Maybe they have. Or maybe they've just been replaced in the dead of night every now and then by substitutes. Anyway, the Yappy Dogs like to have a go at me because they say I often hit my face with my tail when I wag it. Once again, they're just wrong. I might occasionally do that but only when curled in a ball or when wiggling my back-half too much. You don't become great by having a go at your neighbours and that's what they need to learn. What do I do? And what could you do if you were in the same situation? Simply rise above it. And if that doesn't work, always wee on the hedge of your critics when you walk past. I know that might be difficult for some of you. But that's the thing with this self-help book. Take from it what you need. The rest is probably aimed at those who aren't so far along the journey to greatness. We're all on a journey. It's just that some have the windows down and their ears flapping around like crazy dogs, and some are on that same journey taking a well-earned rest, snoozing away, as the miles just drive on by.

## Think outside the box –
## unless you're stuck in the box

The last car journey I did was to a meeting of really important people, discussing really important things, in a really important way. I think it was the World Bank or something. Or the World Cup. World something anyway. Having reached my position as a champion of things that can be championed, I get invited to a lot of meetings. This was a meeting about business. Important business. You had to have the right look about you at this meeting, sort of smart and uncomfortable, and you had to ask things of others that you weren't particularly interested in, and neither were they really, but you all had to pretend you were for about two to three hours. There was this person who had to control the meeting. Everyone called him, 'the Chair'. Which struck me as a bit odd. We could all see he was sitting on a chair, but so was everyone else. Except me, I wandered about a bit, and just sat where I found myself to be, sometimes this was in the sun, sometimes this wasn't. I like to keep people guessing where I am; they never know where a question might be coming at them from. Sometimes they asked for questions from 'the Floor'. I think they'd given me that nickname, just as that other guy was known as 'the Chair'. I don't mind having a nickname but 'the Floor' didn't sound very 'super hero' which is the sort of character I like to have. I can't recall what they were talking about now. It might have been about money, or profits, or costs, or papers, or things going up, or things going down, or things not going quite as they would have liked, or risks, or expressions of interest, or expressions of disinterest. I could pretend I'd remembered but then if you went to their minutes (notes of meetings taken by someone who writes down what was actually said at the meetings) you might find out that I was wrong about it and that I didn't do any of the actions that I promised them I would do, in order to improve the thing, or things, that were troubling everyone, and they did look troubled. One or two of them got quite heated in the discussion about something at one point so I thought that would be a good time to leave. I'd said my bit, they had the benefit of my wisdom, the rest they had to sort out. I can only do what I do. And mainly that's inspiring everyone else. My message was: be inspired by my words and actions, but then use your own out-of-the-kennel, blue sky walk thinking. I think they got the message. You could do something similar next time you're in a meeting.

# When you're awake, pay attention, if you have to

A lot of self-help books try to make things that are difficult to understand, slightly easier to understand. They use things like metaphors, story-telling and pictures. And if they don't help you, luckily enough there's always a follow-up book you can buy. Here's a story from my life to help you. It contains a good message on how to become great. So here goes. One of my tips for making very difficult things easy to do, is to pay attention in the first place. And to stop messing about. And we can see that in this following story. Imagine you're in your first year at puppy training class. There's a bunch of people standing around the room who just happen to have dogs, largely struggling first-time owners. You know there's a massive bag of reward treats available – all you have to do is sit, and wait, or raise a paw, or whatever, just simple stuff. Would you listen, do the really simple thing, and then fill up on treats? Of course you would. But not if you were Puppy Class Pablo. While Puppy Class Pablo was in the room at puppy training class, he wasn't exactly 'in the room'. He had a faraway stare with a look in his eyes that said, 'give me a little bit more time'. I think he just liked turning up for the company. I used to say to him, 'concentrate, Puppy Class Pablo, concentrate'. As a born leader, I'd interpret what the puppy class leader wanted and show the other pups how to do it. But sometimes you can't lead them all through the gate to enlightenment and enrichment. Sometimes some pups get left behind. While I graduated (with honours), Puppy Class Pablo was left doing his re-sits, staring out the window, thinking of other things. Otherworldly things.

Puppy Class Pablo

## Chase your dreams, and if you can't do that, chase some birds

'm currently searching for enlightenment as to how to catch birds and squirrels. I've achieved much in my life and that's why I can tell you all about how to achieve things in your life. It's because I've been there, seen it and done it. Global diplomacy, tackling climate change and fighting off wild bears are all in a day's work for me, but I'm not so good at catching pigeons. I also struggle with magpies and squirrels. I try my best, every time, but they always elude me. I don't mind admitting that. To be great, you need to admit your weaknesses. My inability to fly is certainly holding me back, although it is something I'm working on. I'm hoping in my next book to be able to let you know how to learn to fly. Until then, I'm following my dreams and will never give up the chase.

I'm looking forward to the day when I catch the magpie and then we'll look at each other and wonder what to do next. I imagine the bird will congratulate me on my speed and acceleration, my nimble jumping, my anticipation. I'll tell the bird to forget about the discarded food on the grass and spend more time watching out for furry guys like me chasing them for no reason. This is also a good metaphor for you to learn from. Chase your dreams, never give up, and see constant and never-ending failure as your friend. One day your dreams might come true. And if they don't, at least you'll have had plenty of outdoor exercise which can only be good for you.

## Stick to your principles, unless your principles are a bit odd, in which case, stick to someone else's principles

The outdoors is great. It's the home of sticks. My garden has trees at the bottom and is home to a lot of sticks. Sticks are great. But can sticks point the way to greatness? They certainly can. Here's how to do it. Gather together a few sticks from your favourite stick pile, put them in an arrow shape, then lie down at the tip of the arrow shape. The sticks are now pointing to greatness. Try it, you'll feel good. The one thing that's not so great about sticks is that you're not allowed them in the house. No blankets or soft toys in the garden, no sticks in the house – they're rules that are rigidly enforced by people who aren't flexible enough to be creative thinkers.

Some people talk about the 'carrot and stick method' in that sticks are bad and carrots are good. But this needs re-inventing. Carrots are good, but so are sticks. They're both really good. So that saying is wrong. If I need to motivate my team, first of all I offer them a carrot each, then if that doesn't work, I'll give them a stick, and tell them it's a special stick that you're allowed to take into the house from the garden. How much more motivation does anyone need? My only concern is that sometimes, some of them seem to get the wrong end of the stick.

## You only get one time to make a first impression, unless people forget who you are, then you might get another

Puppy Class Pablo has become quite a character now and I'm left wondering whether he needs a new name. Should he be defined by his not terribly impressive appearances at puppy class, or does he need a new descriptor? 'Ex-Puppy Class Pablo' doesn't sound right. I had a word with Puppy Class Pablo about his personal brand and he didn't seem to really get it. I reminded Pablo about one of the lessons to be learnt on the path to greatness – 'when you're awake, pay attention' – and that's when he said we should add the sub-clause, 'if you have to'. Pablo's like that. As for his name, I've considered a re-brand, but others know him as 'Puppy Class Pablo' and I think it suits him. There's also quite a few other Pablos about. I don't know why. Maybe the people who hang about with Pablo dogs are fans of making things sound a bit more Spanish when they're really not. Anyway, what we can learn from this is that sometimes you need to think about what you stand for, and how you're known. Again, I explained this to Puppy Class Pablo and after a long, head sideways thought, he said he might take me up on the idea. He suggested a new name of 'Puppy Class Picasso'. I'm not sure he got it.

What do we want to be known for? What makes us famous? For me, it's simple. Greatness. But for others, I'm not sure they've considered this enough. There's another dog who is very occasionally in the park called Willow. Willow seemed fairly pleasant, we had a bit of a run-around, and then Willow was sick. And then Willow ate her sick. So, the only thing I know about Willow is that she is a sick-eater. That's weird and that's all she is known for by my chums. I actually wish I knew more about Willow so I could talk about other sides of her character and say she's more of a well-rounded individual but I can't. Think of Willow and you think of sick. And that is why she needs to work on her personal brand. And so should you.

Sick Willow

## Sofa, so good, but let's make it more strategic

I'm a strategic dog. I see the bigger picture. I've given lots of talks to world leaders, people in suits, and people in poor-performing sports teams who are really desperate for a win, and one thing I'm always encouraging them to do is to think strategically. Politicians like to talk about who's got the best flag or more tanks, business people like to talk about their excellent Excel spreadsheets, and sports people like to say it was someone else's fault, or the wind, or the sun in their eyes. And I tell all of them, 'don't think big, think biggest'. In this way, I like to tell the story of 'the tennis ball stuck under the sofa' while making the story appear like it's a tale about something almost irrelevant but has a wider, bigger, deeper meaning, although in truth, it doesn't, the story is simply about a tennis ball stuck under the sofa. But the way I tell my story, it makes it sound like I'm being really clever. What happens is when I get a tennis ball stuck under the sofa, rather than me having to move the sofa to get the ball back or me finding a long stick to dislodge the ball and knock it back, I do a sort of puzzled face and when you do that long enough, one of the people around you usually gives in and they have to sort the problem out. And that's the message, go strategic (tennis ball back in my possession), implement the plan (the puzzled, slightly upset face in this case), and achieve the mission (nothing under any sofas, for now).

# The story you tell is more important than the story you smell

Vegan Sydney

So, a tip for greatness is, make up a story. If it's not true, pretend that it is, tell everyone your story and then at the end, nod your head like you know that they now understand that there's a higher meaning to the story, even when there's not. The older you get, either in dog years or human years, you realise no-one knows what they're doing, and pretty much everyone is making it up as they go along, but some are better than others at being serious and making it look like what they're doing is cleverer and more important than what you're doing. Some get worried that they're not good enough to be doing what they're doing – they call this 'imposter syndrome' – but they shouldn't worry because no-one else really understands what you're doing and they don't actually care much because they're too worried about themselves anyway and maybe whether they'll be found out.

I too suffer from imposter syndrome. I tried to impersonate Vegan Sydney from the neighbouring road when the person with Vegan Sydney got a treat bag out on their walk (vegan treats only, of course). However, the woman soon realised I wasn't Vegan Sydney. I'm bigger than her dog, I'm a different colour to Vegan Sydney, and I've never appeared in the local neighbourhood newsletter under the 'Lost Cats and Dogs' section.

Just a few words about Vegan Sydney. Although Vegan Sydney sounds like a boy, she's actually a girl. As you can see, they've spelt 'Sydney' like the city rather than the boy's name. This is confusing to a lot of people, and gave Vegan Sydney some early gender identity issues but she's OK about it now. She's also OK about once having been lost for four days after chasing a tennis ball out of the park gate. They tried to somehow link me in with the missing dog story, saying the ball had 'Bobs' written on it or something, but I wasn't there. I'd already flown to New York for my appearance in the final of International Fluffy Paws. With Vegan Sydney flying out there with me as my sidekick celeb assistant and PR publicist.

## It's great to be present in the presence of greatness

It's worth mentioning here another thing about becoming great. It's good to remain humble despite being world famous. Being a three-times winner of Fluffy Paws could go to any dog's head, but not mine. I don't even talk about being a three-times winner of Fluffy Paws. I leave that to Vegan Sydney, who does all my PR. That way I get all the acclaim while constantly surprising everyone with my humility. My publicist makes sure all the dogs in the neighbourhood know how successful I've been, again. I know that the local dogs all feel better by knowing that they are in the presence of a great dog. The Yappy Dogs claim it's all 'fake chews' of course. They probably think the world is flat and that a dog has never made it onto the moon. They probably don't believe in canine vaccines either. They also say to me that I'm not world famous just because I've added the words 'world famous' in front of my name. While the media know me as 'World Famous Bobs', I ask the dogs on my street to just call me Bobs. That's how I rock 'n' roll. I'm down with the dogs. I'm just a normal, multi-award-winning, world famous dog that happens to be among them. Sometimes though it is a bit like being The Beatles on my street. When I go out for a walk, there's lots of fans, girls screaming, everything in black and white. Although there is only one of me and they were a fab four. And I'm a dog and they weren't.

## Where it all began –
## raised in the valley of wolves

I t's probably worth me letting you know a few things about my background so let me take you on a magical mystery tour. Many of you reading this will know all about my early days and path to greatness, but some of you will be less aware. Don't worry about that, you can learn more now. And it's much better if you read the next bit in the style of someone narrating the introduction of a dramatic movie, that's what I do, so here goes… 'Bobs was raised in the valley of wolves, near the sound of the chase, nurtured within a pack of suburban cockapoos, destined for glory, stimulated by meal-time treat toys and bouncy play equipment. Of the litter he was last to be chosen but first to bark and first to embark on an adventure like no other. He was given the name, Bobs, or as the world would soon come to know him, 'World Famous Bobs, the world's highest achieving dog'.

I left home at an early age, at nine weeks, Kennel Club registered, microchipped, personalised goodie bag, and ventured from west to east, ready to forge my identity and forage in the bushes for toxic plants that then had to be removed from a garden that would never look the same again. The new people I lived with offered a happy home (but now with added muddy paw prints, chewed edge of sofa, a not-so-good lawn and some shoes that have to be kept above my head height). However, I missed my mum, brothers and sisters and vowed one day to return to the family home, to bring together our dynasty, and this was indeed achieved when a puppy meet-up was arranged. The gathering was in a rented puppy-friendly secure field although I like to think of it as a wooded cliff-top somewhere in the Molineux mountains, with a sun setting in darkening skies over a deep ravine, and me and my cockapoo brethren howling at the rising moon, ready to advance as a pack, some groomed, some needing a bit of a haircut, on a journey like no other, a story like no other, our destiny finally within reach although sometimes put away in the drawer with the harness, lead and dog toys.

# TWO

Learning that the hole is greater
than the sum of the parts

The second step on the
footpath to greatness

## Teamwork makes the dream work, if the dream is easily achievable

They say, 'there's no 'I' in 'team'.' I'm a firm believer I wouldn't be where I am today without my team. Rearrange the letters of 'team' and what have you got? 'Meat' and 'mate' and I like to meet my meat-loving mates* in the park for regular team meetings. The asterisk is there due to Vegan Sydney and her specific food preferences. I've also gone vegan between mealtimes recently. There's quite a few of us behind Brand Bobs who meet in the park including Vegan Sydney, Puppy Class Pablo, the Dog with No Name and the Yappy Dogs (they're never invited but they always seem to be in the park, like omnipresent, territorially aggressive, miserabilists who have got out of the wrong side of the dog basket in the morning, once again).

Vegan Sydney suggested in a recent team meeting that we should give greater consideration to the issue of global sustainability. Everyone contributed some ideas in a brainstorming session except Puppy Class Pablo who was keeping an eye on a pigeon for me in a distant tree. Sydney said the best idea was mine – wearing coats with solar panels on in the summer. The energy we generate could help tackle climate change and raise my profile further. The Yappy Dogs doubted the science behind my idea, just as they doubt the science behind anything, but Puppy Class Pablo said if I had thought of it, he was sure it would work. I'm getting to really like Puppy Class Pablo. Puppy Class Pablo also said the pigeon was still in the tree. The Dog with No Name, with no hint of irony, said the solar panels coat product needed a name. 'Suncoats', I said. 'You already have raincoats, now we have suncoats'.

The Dog with No Name

## In space no-one can you hear dream

A thing that people say is, 'space is the final front ear'. I don't understand why they say that but space is going to be our next park project, after we have successfully launched our suncoats™. It turns out that Puppy Class Pablo is not just a daydreamer, he's looking beyond the birds in the trees to the distant horizons of space. He says he's got plans to transport us into space. This would make us the first pack of dogs in space since the Russian dogs, or were they monkeys? Maybe it was a dog and a monkey, maybe a cat and a squirrel too, although I would worry about the team dynamics there. As a great leader, you've got to ensure that your team pulls together, rather than having a very slow game of zero-gravity chase which could end up in fewer astronauts returning than went out.

I quizzed Puppy Class Pablo about the details of his plans to exit our atmosphere for deep space and he said he hadn't got further yet than getting the team together on the highest bit of the park and jumping. We might be earth-bound for some time but I applaud Puppy Class Pablo for thinking big. I think once we've all managed to jump and reach the pigeon in the tree, we're going to work up the space idea a bit more. One small step at a time. Or rather, one small step for dogs; one giant leap for dogkind. Sometimes that's all it takes.

## Don't just be good at sport, be a good sport

B ack to being great. I'm well-known for greatness in sport. I've won medals in many different sports. I don't wear my medals all the time because that would be a bit clanky. The Yappy Dogs say I've only got one medal, which I do wear, which has my name, phone number and address on (next to my collar) in case I get lost. Again, they're wrong. The medals and cups are all in my trophy cabinet. I've won world cups in football, baseball, handball, frisbee, fetch, the lot. Once again, the Yappy Dogs have been claiming otherwise. The Yappy Dogs say I can't even fetch properly. They say I'm OK at chasing the ball, that I'm not always so good at finding it, and I'm rubbish at letting go of the ball when I bring it back. The Yappy Dogs also claim that there's not even a world cup for fetch. They say that even if there was, no-one would watch it because it's not even a sport. The Yappy Dogs live in ignorance and misery; that's not my fault.

The Day-Glo Pugs (so named because they're always in hi-vis in the park, even on sunny days, it's weird) have said they believe me and they know their stuff. The Day-

The Day-Glo Pugs

Glo Pugs are no mugs. So, to be great: believe in others, believe in yourself, believe in things even when they sound a bit ridiculous, and (this next point was asked to be added in by the Day-Glo Pugs) when it gets dark, make sure you can be seen. If you're a burglar, though, try not to be seen in the dark. I'm not giving burglars any tips on how to be great at stealing things, that's wrong, although I am ace at stealing socks, garlic bread and jigsaw pieces. Talking of jigsaws, an early dream of mine was to work as a jigsaw cardboard taster in the jigsaw-making factory. The Yappy Dogs said that such a job doesn't exist but that's them being negative again. My other dream was to work as a take-away delivery bike rider but the company wouldn't agree to my request that I mainly wanted to pick up the chicken meal orders, especially the chicken orders with the special seasoning. The company was highly inflexible and that's their loss.

## Kindness is the meal deal of life – you know it makes sense

On your journey to becoming great, it's important that you occasionally stop and rest, maybe have a sandwich, and discover the value of kindness. Every day I like to do a random act of kindness. It could be offering to buy someone a coffee at the Hound of the Basket Meals hot food van (although I generally tend to carry sticks rather than money, and the Hound of the Basket Meals doesn't accept sticks as payment, I know, I've tried); it could be offering Puppy Class Pablo one of my indoor sticks for free (people will tend to know indoor sticks as 'pens' or 'pencils' although some will appreciate their true meaning); it could be offering an initial discount period on one of my online masterclass business network marketing schemes (this has nothing to do with pyramid selling, although if you get in early you'll get more bark for your bite); or it could be inviting the team round to mine to watch my TED talk again, allowing them to comment about which bits were best. Sometimes I joke, sometimes I have been known to very occasionally make one or two things up, but one thing I do know: kindness is the companion of the truly blessed, it is the river that feeds the oceans. And if kindness and puppy eyes don't work, lick them, that'll cheer them up.

## Best to get on the same page – unless you're reading different books

The other day I hit the ground running on a level playing field, getting some ducks in a row, when someone moved the goalposts, before kicking a ball into the long grass. Vegan Sydney said it sounded like I was trapped in a terrible world of business jargon. No, I said, I was doing my business in the park.

## Aim for the common ground,
## if you know the way there

The park, as you may have noticed, is where a lot of things happen. It's where I've previously held a meeting of the G7 (seven retired greyhounds). The meeting ended suddenly before the agenda was finished when a rabbit was spotted – they couldn't work out why the rabbit didn't run away at a steady speed in an oval circuit around the park. I have also hosted the Global Security Council there although it could have been a summit of Thunderbirds, I can't quite remember. It might not have been Thunderbirds as no puppet-piloted spacecraft emerged from anywhere near the row of RIP bench seats so it probably was the Global Security people. I have a busy life so it's difficult sometimes to remember all the big things I've done.

I was chairing the Global Security Council at the time, which was considering things happening in our park, at a point when we were facing an arms escalation crisis. It was getting out of control. Puppy Class Pablo's stick had been stolen by one of the Yappy Dogs. The Dog with No Name decided to take matters into his own paws by getting a bigger stick. I was about to try to pick up and carry an even bigger stick, it makes my jaws ache to think about it, when I realised enough is enough. This had got to stop. I called a meeting of the Global Security Council at RIP Bench Seat Hill and carefully negotiated a truce. Peace had broken out across the park and all dogs were happy to pick up sticks roughly equivalent to their own dog size. There was no one-updogship anymore. In the park now, we are all equal, all sticks are equal. Vegan Sydney said it was a diplomatic triumph. Sometimes on your journey to greatness, it's about bringing others together, finding the common ground, and then burying your bones of animosity within. That's what I do. You should too.

## If you can't handle fame, don't go to the park a lot

One of the potential problems of greatness is fame and how you handle it. I'm always being recognised in the street or in the park; fans are always wanting to have their selfie photos taken with me. Some recognise me from my lead role in the James Bond re-make, *The Dog with The Golden Paws*, and some from the local 'lost dog' posters nailed onto our road's trees (it wasn't me, just a dog who looked a bit like me, but not so 'movie star'). Fans ask me about my trips into space, climbing Everest, scuba diving the depths of the deepest oceans, and how I effortlessly carry fairly large sticks that look almost too big to carry. I'm famous, the world's highest achieving dog, but out on the street, I'm just plain old Bobs. Some people call me 'Waffle' though due to my similarities to a television dog (it's on a channel called *CBeebies*, watched by some of the smaller people in the world, the ones that seem generally happier than the bigger people). The bigger people have said a few times to me, 'it's Basil Brush' but I don't use the 'boom, boom' catchphrase and he's a fox and I'm a dog. Different animals. I don't disappoint them, however; if they want to think they've met the wonder dog (or a fox), not the world's highest achieving dog, then that's fine. I'm a dream maker, not a dream breaker. Puppy Class Pablo sometimes still gets confused and calls me Waffle but he does watch a lot of TV. Probably too much.

When you're heading for the heights, don't look down; unless there's a big drop in front of you, in which case it's worth looking down

For my Everest adventure, fans want to know how I became the first dog to climb the world's highest peak. I'll tell you how I did it. I just carried on walking. I was on a fund-raising trek to Everest base camp and simply did not stop, despite having a bit of snow caught up in my fur and an icy nose. It was cold, yes, but it was fun. After base camp, I just carried on walking on the ladders across the ice fall crevasses, negotiated my way up from camps one to four, outpaced the yeti, jumped up the ice shelf using ice pick claws and wandered along the ridge to the summit. As quick as you can say, 'Bobs, you're amazing!' I was on top of the world. It was easy to do. I'd done lots of training, climbing up snowmen on winter days to eat their carrot noses, so didn't need extra oxygen or a team of smiley Sherpas carrying things and drinking tea. I then ran back down the mountain and had a big dinner. The rest of the base camp trek fund-raising team were delighted to see my photos from the top of Everest. They said, 'Bobs, now you really are, literally, the world's highest achieving dog'. I smiled. Well, I would have if I could. I don't have the most natural smile and I was bit icy. Instead, I just wagged my tail, in a knowing, mountaineer kind of way. Vegan Sydney arranged some satellite TV interviews for me before I ran across the Himalayas to become the first K9 on K2.

The Yappy Dogs were interviewed on TV around that time, saying the only place I'd climbed was the 'land of make believe'. They looked pretty stupid though when I showed them photos of me on top of Everest and K2, and standing next to the north and south poles, which I embarked upon shortly afterwards. The Yappy Dogs, cynical and snappy as ever, said they had brought in an 'expert' (moany person) who assessed my photographic evidence as being pictures of famous snowy places with the same cut-out photo of me Sellotaped on top. Their claims were widely discredited at a presentation I gave at the Royal Geographical Society in London. A survey distributed at the event (with a free bone upon completion), to various attendees including Puppy Class Pablo, the Dog with No Name, and the Day-Glo Pugs, found 100% of them believed me. Made to look the fools they are, the Yappy Dogs were yapping no more after that.

# Keeping up with the influencers

**B**eing world famous has also made me something of an 'influencer' on social media. I'm not entirely sure what an influencer is but Vegan Sydney explained it as a way for people who have no reason to be famous, to usually go somewhere very sunny and demonstrate their general lack of intelligence but also their photo editing skills. Vegan Sydney said there were also some influencers who were nice and clever and I was one of those. Vegan Sydney said as well as posting videos of me negotiating difficult peace deals between countries at war, or showing off my stick collection (some are longer than others), I should record a funny dance video but I'm not sure. I seem to be enough of an influencer anyway. They say, 'if you're not on social, you're not part of the conversation'. But I know Sick Willow's on Insta and I'm not sure I'd like to be part of that conversation at all.

Also, there's a poodle I used to know, @FabOliviaPooch, who I still follow on social media. She goes on and on about her expensive and exotic summer holidays, her expensive and exclusive skiing holidays, the amazing things anyone in her family does ('so proud of so and so

passing an examination about something, bla, bla, bla…').
I'm world famous and I don't tell anyone about it. Much.
Even though @FabOliviaPooch says the same things all
the time, I still follow her because in her profile picture she
hasn't noticed that behind her there's a poo bag hanging
from a tree. Why do people do that? Put poo bags in trees,
that is. Not taking photos of poo bags in trees. That would
be even more weird.

#LivingTheDream

@FabOliviaPooch

## Stick with what you know, unless what you know isn't doing you any favours

There's something we can learn from @FabOliviaPooch. And that's not to boast all the time. And linked to that is a further lesson about greatness: you can't be great at everything. And actually, there's some things even I'm not good at. I've become world famous in politics, sport, business and many other things. My book on 'how to behave nicely for the dog groomer' was top of the dog grooming behavioural guides' bestsellers chart for a long time. But on my path to greatness were many wrong turns, broken paving stones and cars parked particularly badly.

Here are some of my mistakes and I'm happy to share them. We can all learn from our mistakes. Early on in my career I joined the police dogs' team, to help lead them to baddies, using my special detective powers. But I only reached the rank of 'sniffy dog' rather than 'sniffer dog'. I was an enthusiastic pup and thought the police would like to know where all the pavement elastic bands and dropped gloves were. The detective said my 'evidence' would only convict postmen and small children with cold hands. I re-trained and became a greyhound dog. I'm pretty quick but those official greyhounds are something else. I struggled to fit in the box at the start of the races and got a bit distracted during the running bit. On reflection, the fact that I'm not a greyhound seemed to be the biggest obstacle in becoming an approved racing greyhound dog. It's a barrier that doesn't need to be there and I've raised it with the greyhound association. Anyway, not sure it was a great job anyway. All the greyhounds I've ever met since are 'retired'. It's not even a good retired where you get to spend all your time on the beach in Spain. The lesson for greatness though is know your strengths and weaknesses. If you're not a greyhound, you're just not a greyhound. You're something else.

## On the path to greatness,
## don't eat things off it

Thom Yorkie

In the words of the great Martin Luther King, 'I have a dream', and I have a dream whereby I'm on my morning walk and I bump into Thom Yorkie. Thom Yorkie isn't really his name. He's actually called 'Ruffles' but Vegan Sydney says he looks like a famous rock singer with that name except the famous singer is not a Yorkie terrier.

They're also both a bit angry at the world. Thom Yorkie tells me to eat something funny looking on the path as a dare. I do and then things get a bit spinney, and I end up time travelling, back in time and I go to Amsterdam and sit between John Lennon and Yoko Ono in their bed, which annoys them a bit, and while they're protesting for more peace in the world, I'm trying to tell the TV news crews that the fake plastic trees in the corner of the room need watering and I'm the dog to help; and then things get more spinney and colourful, and later I wake up in the vets and Kennford Kenn, our local alliterative vet, tells me I've eaten something I shouldn't have, again. And then I have to have pills hidden in my meals for all of the following week, and I don't know whether it was a dream at all. But I do know I tend to avoid Thom Yorkie on my morning walks as much as possible now. When I see Thom Yorkie I tend to run around him. Or put my headphones on, pretend Thom's not there, and listen to the wonderful, uplifting music of Bob Marley, or the thoughtful music of Bob Dylan or any famous Bob for that matter. Listening to famous Bob music makes me less worried about Thom Yorkie, his intense scowl and devious psychological tricks. You should do this too. Put on Bob music during times of trouble. It'll help.

# THREE

Time to check the map
and what's for lunch

The third step on the
footpath to greatness

## If you don't know the answer to the question, it was probably the wrong question

**B**efore I go on, I think it might be worth a bit of a recap on lessons learnt to date. There's some pretty tricky stuff coming up, which is aimed more at black belt masters of greatness. So, let's check your understanding so far with my quiz, which I like to call 'Pupmaster'. If you know the answers to the following questions, or can pretend you know, or are able to look them up on the internet really quickly, then you'll be OK to move on to the next stage.

So, if you're sitting around a table full of world leaders and one of them says, 'if you steal all the ham off the table when none of us world leaders are looking, then the world just might blow up,' what would you do?

If you're about to set off into space when you look out of your rocket and see a nice stick on the ground and then the mission command person says, 'everybody OK for lift-off?' what would you do?

If you're about to conquer Everest and your climbing pal says, 'there's only enough oxygen left for one us to go to the top but I've heard base camp has just had a big delivery of pizza,' what would you do?

Now, let's move on to this famous riddle, which I have adapted slightly. Let's see how well you do. A man has to get me, a squirrel, and a box of specially seasoned chicken across a river. He has a rowboat, and it can only carry him and one other thing. If World Famous Bobs and the specially seasoned chicken are left together, World Famous Bobs will eat the chicken. If the specially seasoned chicken and the squirrel are left together, the squirrel will probably bury the chicken because that's all they seem to do, bury things, apart from leaping between trees. If World Famous Bobs and the squirrel are left together, it could be mayhem. How does the man do it? If you worked it out, well done. Now, repeat the exercise, this time, with the man having a hole in his wooden rowboat, and a crocodile or two in the water, one of the crocodiles operating a chainsaw. How did you do? I'm sure you solved everything. You can now move on to the next stage.

## How to put the 'maze' in 'amazing' without getting lost in a hedge

Those questions were tricky. No-one said learning how to become great was easy. But you must have answered correctly because you're still with us. Or you've just ignored the questions and carried on reading anyway; that's fine too (that makes you a 'disrupter', someone who challenges the status quo, someone who truly can shake up the system). Now, onto the next level. However, reaching the next level of greatness is like something you've been chewing that you shouldn't have and has been taken off you and put on a shelf you can't reach. Like a sock or a face mask. This next bit will teach you how to recover the sock, against all odds.

In answering the Pupmaster questions you will have realised that it's one for all and all for one, that the muskehounds are always ready, helping everybody. That was demonstrated the other day in the park at the RIP benches. The team had gathered together at our usual meeting spot when Puppy Class Pablo arrived wearing the infamous cone of shame and a slightly sad expression. We knew the job we had to do and I led the way. Before long we had removed the cone of shame, Vegan Sydney had transformed it into a modern classic lampshade and Puppy Class Pablo was soon the envy of the park. Guess who was later seen running down Muddy Hill, near the new housing development, with a cone of shame removed, replaced by a modern classic lampshade/attractive hat on their head, as the newly-crowned and self-declared 'king of the paaark'? Go Puppy Class Pablo!

By way of explanation, what we did here was to put some of our earlier 'how to be great' thinking all together: leadership (me), creative thinking and arts and crafts skills (Vegan Sydney), and teamwork (all) to remove the cone (all the team, except the Dog with No Name who by then had gone back for his dinner).

Up until this point you've been learning individual lessons on becoming great. Put these lessons together and 'great' becomes 'greater', 'good' becomes 'gooder', and 'amazing' becomes 'amazinger'. Well, at least 'great' becomes 'greater', I'm not so sure about the other two looking back. But what I did on *my* journey was even more special, 'greater' became the 'greatest' and I'll tell you a bit more about how I did it now...

## Wrong time, right place, or right time, wrong place? You make the call

After settling in with my family, they took me to puppy class, and upon graduation I went to the school of life. It was there that I learnt the importance of moving things that were in one place to another, different place. Same item, but now placed somewhere different. Not all dogs get this. And I think this marked me out for greatness. I noticed, for example, that some sticks on the daily walk were not always in the right place. By the end of each walk, the sticks were in a much better place, usually left outside the front door upon our return. Furthermore, I noticed that some toys and chews that were in the house, sometimes would be better placed in the garden, and at other times, realised that those toys and chews might be better off returned inside. Moving things from one place to another place is an important part of how the world works. Everything in the right place, as Thom Yorkie once told me, before then looking like he was going to bite me. That's the thing with Thom Yorkie. Take his words of advice and then retreat to a safe distance quickly.

Since leaving my brothers and sisters, I've always lived with the same family. They're nice people to live with. Even though the Earth spins quite nicely without their help, humans think they're in control of the world so it's good to understand humans better by living with them; that way you can help them more and help the planet more. The people I live with are around most of the time, one of them always seems to turn up on my morning and afternoon walks (often saying things like 'drop' or 'leave it' as we walk together for some reason). When they're not around and the house is occasionally empty, I like to play FIFA on the Xbox in the lounge or sit in the swing seat in the garden with a mocktail. Or I might go and sit in the office and write my latest novel. I've no pups of my own yet. The celeb magazines seem to think I'm in a relationship with Vegan Sydney and are asking when a litter might be on the way. But the only litter I'm interested in at the moment is moving plastic bottles and bags along the morning walk, picking them up and dropping them later so they're in a different place. The right place.

# Don't judge a book by its cover, if it hasn't got a cover

I mentioned just now my novels. I'd like to become a literary great. Like Charles Dickens, Jane Austen or that person who wrote the Snoopy books – all about a dog who sleeps on top of his kennel. Genius. I haven't as yet though had a novel published. The slight hold-up has been that I haven't got beyond the first line in any of my soon-to-be classic novels. I'm OK with writing the first line. Some of my first lines are up there with the best. But even in the best of times, and the worst of times, I've struggled with what I call, 'the difficult second sentence'. However, I think I've recently made a break-through. I've dreamt up a second sentence that you can use in any novel, anywhere, and it makes the first line even better. My new second line is this, "However, that was not necessarily true". You can add it into any book to make it better. With this all-new, inspirational second line, my writer's block has been unblocked and I'm now well into the third and fourth sentences of my new soon-to-be blockbuster book. It's called 'Good grief, Charlie Brown' and is about a dog who sleeps on the garden shed, because he doesn't have a kennel, and is nothing like those Snoopy books at all. Vegan Sydney said something about it did sound familiar to her. But then again, she's read a lot of books.

## How to put the 'compass' in 'compassion'

So, onwards and upwards, or sideways. With my new novel only several hundred pages away from completion, I've been able to concentrate on other matters. And top of the list has been completing this very helpful, really factual self-help guide to becoming greater than you currently are. And I want to tell you now a little bit more about how to do that. My big tip here is, 'don't know your limits'. If you do already know your limits, see if you can forget them a bit. Try running around in a circle, then jump on and off sofas, then run around a bit more, that should help you forget. I find limits too limiting.

Without limits, we are free to conquer the world. Like reaching the Poles. If you exclude the odd passing penguin or polar bear, or maybe seagull (they're everywhere, like magpies), people have always made a big thing about reaching the North Pole and South Pole. It is a bit tricky. I've done it a few times. And when I last did it, I overcame a bit of bad luck. On the trips when I got to the top and bottom of the Earth, it happened to be really quite cold and snowy. I'd imagined it would normally look a lot less

Christmassy than it actually did. I hadn't planned for snow, possibly because I'd appointed Puppy Class Pablo as head of research and planning for the expeditions. Puppy Class Pablo hadn't mentioned snow or cold weather in any of my pre-polar briefings.

The North Pole and South Pole have been an adventure destination for decades. I'm glad I went but after reaching them, I knew I wanted to go one better. It was then I came up with 'the brilliant idea'. The sort of idea that could only belong to a great dog. I was going to become the first dog – or person – to reach the West Pole and the East Pole. Making the full compass! Leaving my limits back at home, along with my passport, which made for a difficult start to the journey, I walked, sniffed, and ran along the equator, sticking a couple of flags in the ground along the way, and helpfully painting a white line around the middle of the Earth so others could easily follow my journey. Upon returning home, a campaign was launched to re-name the equator as 'Bob's Latitude'. That's very kind of everyone who backed the campaign but the equator belongs to the world, not just a very brave, energetic and truly inspiring dog who has travelled to the four poles of the Earth.

The Yappy Dogs across the road said the campaign was just a failed PR stunt dreamt up by Vegan Sydney in order to boost my fame ahead of the launch of my new novel based on a laid-back dog that gets off the top of his garden shed to walk around the Earth. But once again, that's the Yappy Dogs showing how cynical and spiteful they can be. Let them yap, I say. I've got flags in the four corners of the world. Or I would have if Puppy Class Pablo had remembered to pack flags.

## Feel the fear and do it anyway, unless it's really scary and then you might wish to reconsider

Vegan Sydney may be accused of arranging PR stunts but many of you will know that I am used to performing stunts of my own, as a famous movie stunt dog. I'm famous in Hollywood, Bollywood, Cricklewood and the local wood for performing all my own stunts although my long-time look-a-like 'Flash' has been known to step in on most occasions. Flash is maybe a little smaller than me, and doesn't have my distinctive white tummy marking, and according to Vegan Sydney, is not quite as good-looking as me, but if you squint your eyes and don't pay too much attention, he looks a bit like me.

I earned the Hollywood nickname of 'brave Bobs' when I was chosen for the part of Evel Knievel in a film about his life, a bio-pic it's called. They'd originally offered the part to Tom Hanks but my friend Tom said it would better suit a dog, someone whose ears flapped around a bit more when riding the motorbike. Tom's often recommending me for movie roles and is currently looking at doing some re-makes of his old films, just so he can team up with me more. There are scripts ready now for *Sleepless in Seattle Due to the Barking Dog Next Door*, *Bridge of Spies and Spaniels*, and *Saving Private Ryan's Dog*.

'Sniffles' Flash, Bobs' stunt double

I practised for the *Evel Knievel Cockapoo* film by riding a motorbike around town and jumping over bridges and buses but on the film set at Caesars Palace in Las Vegas I sensed something was wrong. The big scene was to feature the great Evel Knievel Cockapoo jumping his motorbike over the fountains, outside the front of the casino. I have a nose for trouble and the fact that they'd moved the landing ramp to the wrong place on the other side of the fountains made me think 'Sniffles' Flash might be better suited and want to stand in for a well-paid job. 'Sniffles' Flash has no nose for trouble or much sense of smell at all. Flash likes a challenge. We're great pals, Flash and me, and he's always saying, 'brave Bobs, just let me have a go, just let me have a go'. And this is the learning about being great from this story. Even though there was the chance for me to do the 151-feet jump myself and gain all the praise and attention, this time I let Flash do it. There's enough fame and glory to go round for everyone. So, Flash did the jump, and he is now recovering well. And I'm trying to see whether he might be able to help out in the planned sequel, *Evel Knievel Cockatoo*.

## The answers are within you, you just need to find the right dog to ask you the questions

Let's mention here something I've been wanting to say for a while. To become great, and that's why you're probably reading this, you need to give something back, and I'm not talking here about the tennis ball I temporarily stole by complete accident from that spaniel in the park the other day, who didn't seem interested in it anyway. I'm talking about giving something back to the community. I like to do my bit to help people. People have always been very kind to me. Apart from that person who was with the spaniel who got all shouty about tennis ball theft. You would have thought it was a really special tennis ball, like something they would play with at Wimbledog.

I like helping people. That's why I became… a therapy dog! I was asked to help out because of my kind nature, the fact that I'm a super furry animal, and that the Yappy Dogs had previously abysmally failed. It was a while back now when the Yappy Dogs were invited into the local school to be therapy dogs for the students. Unfortunately, but maybe not surprisingly, it didn't go to plan. The Yappy Dogs just did their annoying yapping and looked miserable and a bit aggressive if anyone came too near them. Also, the Yappy Dogs weren't very positive. They told the students that exams were really hard and if they failed them, it would seriously affect their job prospects and life chances, possibly leading to a lifetime of insecure employment and personal unfulfillment. After that episode, the school needed a proper therapy dog – one that would not only look nice and cuddly but say the right things. Step forward Bobs to save the day!

The Yappy Dogs said I didn't have the training and skills to become a therapy dog, but what do they know? I'm a natural at this sort of stuff. I don't tend to listen to the Yappy Dogs anyway. For example, they said no-one is going to watch *Evel Knievel Cockatoo* because it sounded like a rubbish film. They said *Empire* magazine described it as sounding just like the original movie with the only difference being a bird instead of a dog doing the motorbike stunts. It was at that moment that a bag of dog treats (*'Bobs' special super smoky sausage'*) somehow whacked one of the Yappy Dogs in the face, which, for once, stopped their yapping. To this day, no-one knows how that bag of treats for the *'wonder dog in your life'* (with my picture on the front cover, no less!) somehow ended up being flung at the Yappy Dogs. The fact that we receive bulk free deliveries of the product due to a carefully negotiated Vegan Sydney marketing deal is purely coincidental. While the Yappy Dogs were still stunned from being hit by a bag of the finest dog treats, Puppy Class Pablo was careful to pick up the bag and eat all the contents to avoid anything dangerous like that ever happening again.

Anyway, back to my life as a therapy dog. I've been providing therapy for the local students, and latterly teachers, ever since the Yappy Dogs were banned from the school. They appreciate my calm personality and positive outlook. I've extended my therapy service offer to include counselling and have worked with businesses and sports clubs.

A big football club once asked me in to have a counselling session with their mis-firing striker who had stopped scoring goals. The key to counselling is to encourage the person to find their own answers rather than you telling them what to do. I helpfully asked him open questions like, 'when you take a shot, why don't you shoot on target at the goal?' and things like that. I asked him, 'instead of missing all the time and annoying your team-mates and fans, why don't you try scoring?' It was very successful and it was obvious I was pretty great at counselling. Now you're going to ask, 'so, did he score in the very next game then, Bobs?' Well, no, he didn't. Nor in the next game. Or the one after that. He was rubbish and got transferred at the end of the season to a small club in Spain where in the summer locals and tourists now throw rotten tomatoes at him as part of the town's annual fiesta celebrations. My counselling obviously helped him to pursue a career he'd previously never thought of as a summer salad vegetable target, living nearer to the Mediterranean, and I'm sure he's enormously grateful.

## After a run of defeats, you can always be today's champion, or runner-up

I remember the day well. The day when I first became a much-valued 'mental health champion'. Having volunteered as a therapy dog and enthusiastic but not formally trained counsellor, the progression to becoming a mental health champion was logical. This is all part of the process of becoming great – you have to give in order to receive, and the path to happiness and fulfilment is generally found through making others happy.

The day when I stepped up to becoming a mental health champion was one of those lovely, sunny, leaves gently blowing in the trees, squirrels still annoyingly out-of-reach, park days. You would have expected the team to be full of the joys of late spring but a local cloud of gloom had descended. I had been turned down for the part in the latest 007 James Bond film, *Quantum of Spaniels*, which had caused Vegan Sydney, my publicist and also acting agent, to doubt her skills. The Dog with No Name had been playing in the park pond and was now regretting getting so muddy, and had misplaced his old tennis ball. Puppy

Class Pablo was feeling down after he found out that the hot food snack he thought he'd invented that was proudly going to make him millions – noodles in a pot where you simply add hot water – and which he had named '*Not Poodles*' – had already been invented and had been selling in the shops for years with a much better name.

There wasn't much of a smile about in our team that day. So, what did I do? I found the old tennis ball of the Dog with No Name that I had been keeping safe in my mouth since his pond dip and organised a quick game of chase ball; told the team about a fascinating fact (something about the speed of the Earth spinning that I wasn't entirely sure about, I said something like a thousand miles an hour, I mean, who knows); and told them that sometimes it's OK not to be OK. We all get down sometimes. That's just how it is. Don't expect to be great and happy all the time. It won't be like that, because it's not. Sometimes, the big black dog sits behind all of us.

And later, when Vegan Sydney got back to her office, she found out why they had declined me for *Quantum of Spaniels*. The reason being that the BBC had already signed me up to become the first Dogtor Who and the filming commitments clashed. The script for the new feature-length *Dogtor Who and the Pyramid in the Park* episode was amazing. I was due to bump into my old nemesis, the Cydermen, at the park bench, near to the spooky orchard of fallen apples. This filming clash between Dogtor Who and James Bond was troubling me though. If only there were two of me – and then I had my bright idea. Maybe 'Sniffles' Flash could play my character in filming James Bond until I had finished recording my scenes as the time-travelling, Tardis-driving, half-human, half-alien, but now mostly furry dog-based creature carrying a sonic stick. Flash said that would be fine if the film studio was happy that the James Bond accomplice was now not only a dog, but a dog on crutches. Vegan Sydney put in a call.

'Dogtor Who and the Cydermen'

## Reasons to be cheerful,
## one, two, three...

Vegan Sydney is a very optimistic dog. She never takes 'no' for an answer. Unless the right answer to the question is 'no' and then she'll accept that. If you had to describe Sydney in one word it would be 'cheerful'. Which is a nice characteristic to have. She was less cheerful when I tried to practise my new skills as a vet acupuncturist on her, which I'd learnt off *YouTube,* but she's forgiven me now. She looked like a bad hedgehog.

Not everyone is cheerful though. And trying to be great can bring its pressures. That's why I've developed a list of reasons to be cheerful. You could start writing one of your own. Here's mine so far: trees and lamp-posts, running for a treat, an interesting new stick, someone near me on a sofa, someone coming through the front door, someone saying 'din-dins', an absent-minded bird, a cold carrot, a warm summer lawn, catching snow fall, a dog meet-up in the park, dropped food, an open dishwasher with gravy plates, the countryside, clothes drying in the wind at a jumpable height, pretty much all smells, weekend mornings sleeping through a film, a new chew to hide under cushions, pretending a soft toy is a wild animal in a game of 'predator and prey', any advances in reversing climate change, and anything or anyone that is a force for good in this world. That probably includes you.

There are many reasons to be cheerful. Have a mindful moment and think about them. Feel the air in your furry ears or maybe not-so-furry ears, listen to the sound of morning birdsong, feel the sun on your back, savour the texture of a stolen piece of fabric, watch the blackbirds on the fence, feel the damp grass under your paws or toes, and appreciate this moment now because this moment will pass, and the next moment might not be as good. Sick Willow might turn up in the next moment and be ill again. Right next to you.

## The light at the end of the tunnel could just be a reflective harness

To be great, your mental health is hugely important. So too, of course, is your physical health. You need your head and body and four legs, or maybe a few fewer legs, all working together. I'm a regular at our local *barkrun*, a free run around the park that takes place every Saturday morning. If you take part, you have to have a human connected via a lead so they can enjoy it too, and you need to remember your barkcode so they can scan in your time at the finish.

I first realised the link between physical health and greatness a couple of years ago. It happened when, *mid-barkrun*, I spotted Stop Start Freddie trapped in the tunnel at the dog agility course in the park, with his running pal trying to release him by pushing his behind. It wasn't Stop Start Freddie's greatest moment, and try as I might, I can't forget the image of the bulky golden retriever stuck half-way into the tunnel of gloom and going no further. I also can't forget as the video I took at the time has now totalled up thousands of viewers on my *YouTube* channel. If you were wondering, and it's not relevant but it might need an explanation, Stop Start Freddie was so named because he always lies down when he sees another dog on a walk before taking off again. Stop Start Freddie seems to exercise a fair bit but must really over-do meal times. Or maybe it's treats between meals. Maybe the fridge door doesn't shut properly. He's a big cuddly chap. You wouldn't want to shout 'pile on' in the park and see Stop Start Freddie bounding towards you, stopping occasionally en route of course. Puppy Class Pablo said he once needed to go for a check-up after Stop Start Freddie bounced into him, after he got between Freddie and the ice cream van.

It was this now famous incident in the dog agility course that persuaded me to achieve a position of greatness in the medical profession... I studied to become a consultant in puppy-lick health. I'm now often being interviewed in the media when there's a story about canine illness or injury. I wear a white coat and have some bones on my desk so it looks like I know about parts of the body. 'Should a dog eat poisonous, old things, Dr Bobs?' the media ask. No. 'Should a dog exercise regularly, Dr Bobs?' Yes. 'Should a dog smoke, Dr Bobs?' No. 'Should a dog drink from muddy water, Dr Bobs?' No. With this expert knowledge, I can help animals, and humans too for that matter, be the best they can be. It's more difficult to be great on the outside if things aren't so great on the inside.

So, anyway, back to Stop Start Freddie. Did he ever get out of the dog agility tunnel or is it now just a 'return from the same entrance' attraction? I'm happy to say, thanks to a bit of brute force and one dog's determination to see daylight again, Stop Start Freddie did indeed make the great escape, like something from a war movie where the hero is a big, fat dog prisoner of war who's had too much of the camp's rations. There's now a sign up at the entrance to the tunnel and also at the doggy see-saw with a weight warning and a picture of a sort of cross, upset-looking large dog. Thanks to this helpful new signage, no dog has ever got stuck again. Well, at least not when I've been around to film it.

Stop Start Freddie

# FOUR

Navigating without a compass
using the stars and instinct

The fourth step on the
footpath to greatness

## On a voyage of discovery, you occasionally need to stop at the services

Becoming great is a process of self-education. I remember there was a time when things got a bit much for me. I had to take some time off because I recognised that I was becoming a bit too bitey and barky around the house. Vegan Sydney helped me around that time with a bit of yoga and mindfulness coaching. I would take myself into the garden and just enjoy the moment, listening to the birds, trying not to think too much about the squirrel in the tree. Then I did big science. And that's what ended up landing me the Nobel science prize.

I had worked on a number of scientific research projects. I believe I was the first dog to discover DNA (Digging's Never Appreciated) and the Theory of Relativity (holes in garden fences might be OK for hedgehogs but not for dogs who are now bigger than they once were). It was Puppy Class Pablo who started the ball rolling for my greatest scientific discovery though. One day, as we were admiring the view from the park RIP benches, listening to the sound of young children falling off skateboards, he said to me, 'Bobs, why don't you develop a Theory of Everything that explains and links together everything in the universe?' This wasn't the usual thing that you heard Puppy Class Pablo say. In hindsight, I think he might have been abducted in the night and replaced by a similar-looking but slightly more cerebral creature. I like a challenge as much as the next dog and this was one that I was prepared to accept. I read as much as I could. I got a blackboard where I could write complicated equations. I got a pair of glasses to make me look cleverer. Days turned into nights and nights turned into days.

After quite a while, the eureka moment happened. It happened when I had my paws on the kitchen work top and knocked the fruit bowl over, and an apple, or a banana, hit me on the head. It could have been a pear come to think of it. That's it, I thought. Still dazed from the falling fruit incident, I began to work out how the universe expanded from a single point (the famous 'Big Bang') to get bigger and bigger and bigger, until ultimately, black holes join together, with all the matter in the universe becoming denser and actually collapsing in on itself (something I've called the 'Big Quiet'). Let's now pause for a moment here for you to take all this in. Because it only gets weirder. After that, after the Big Quiet has happened, there will then be another Big Bang. And so on. That's why space and time was never invented. Because it's always been there. Big Bang. Big Quiet. Repeat. Ad infinitum. Or for infinity. Whichever is the longer. My work was then peer-reviewed by a bunch of cockapoos who said it was all probably true. Maybe, or not.

It was great to win the Nobel Prize for my Big Quiet Theory (which I dedicated at the ceremony to my unlikely inspiration, Puppy Class Pablo). However, some of the working out has been disputed by various academics. Dusty old professor Fenny Bentley at Oxbridge University (in a counter-proposal, probably funded by the Yappy Dogs from across the road) said an examination of my blackboard mathematics showed mainly drawings of me next to something that looks not like a black hole but a big hole, and me on hols with Vegan Sydney, along with a list of my favourite treats. People doubted Newton, Einstein and Hawking. They can doubt me too. I worked out why the universe *is*. You don't have to do something as big as that to become great (after all, I've already done it) but setting no limits to what you might be able to do is a good starting point. Be your own Big Bang! But don't literally blow up. That'll get you nowhere.

## Feel the fear of failure and do it anyway, or find a sunny spot to sleep in for a bit, both are equally good

et's not get the idea that the achievement of greatness is failure-free along the way. You have to let failure become your friend. I've previously spoken of some early career jobs that I proved particularly ill-suited for. There's lots of things I've now realised I'm not terribly good at. You just need to find the things that you can do. For me, failure is the F-word. I've tried and failed at fashion (no interest in clothes), floristry (too busy smelling, not enough time spent arranging, apparently), football (two left feet), and financial accounting (no interest in numbers or being a financial accountant).

Sometimes, with failure, when you fall off the skateboard, you just have to get back on and try again. And sometimes when you fall off the skateboard, you have to kick the stupid skateboard, and burn it, or sell it to someone else who doesn't realise how tedious skateboarding is, and how much it hurts when you fall off. It didn't take me long to realise I'm not the kind of crazy slacker dog that likes to hang around abandoned parts of town, finding amusement from balancing on a piece of wood above different slabs of concrete. I'm a dog with places to go, things to do, and mysteries to solve…

## Make sure whoever is in charge of remembering things is good at remembering things

No-one knows where he came from, no-one knows where he's going to, no-one knows his name. The Dog with No Name is a complete mystery. This lovely labrador is often in the park, we've known him for a while, but it's now past the time when you can ask his name without embarrassment. But then the other day… at long last a breakthrough! Puppy Class Pablo, with the skill of a master detective, and the memory of a much, much older dog, heard the Dog with No Name being called by a person in the park. And then the name he heard was… gone.

Puppy Class Pablo had heard the name, but then had almost instantly forgotten. He seemed to think it was something like a King of England might have – Henry, William, James. However, he might have mis-remembered. It actually was more like the name of a celebrity chef – Jamie, Hugh, Gordon. Moments later and Puppy Class Pablo said maybe it could have been a name associated with escape tunnels in *The Great Escape* – Tom, Dick, Harry. For a brief moment therefore, we almost knew the name of the Dog with No Name. We could have called him by his real name. He would have been the Dog with A Name. But being cuddly and anonymous is part of his character. I'm not too disappointed. Some things are just meant to be. The Dog with No Name is his name. I'd actually be disappointed now if he was called Henry or Harry or anything else. Scooby Doo always solved every mystery, but some mysteries are best left hanging in the air, like fog clouding trees in the park on a cold, misty morning, with leaves blowing around in front of your paws. Being great, similarly, might involve a degree of mystery in your personality. Leave some things unknown. Some things have to stay within the *Mystery Machine*.

## When things get a
## bit muddy, dig deeper

It was the Dog with No Name, who briefly once had a name, but who is now still the Dog with No Name, who discovered it. He discovered the Muddy Place. The Muddy Place is in the thicket of trees, which are fenced off to everyone in the park, but where we go in via the small hole in the fence. The Dog with No Name, being bigger than the rest of the team, does struggle to get through the hole, but he always manages it. The Muddy Place is home to many sticks, a few badgers (who we've tried to say hello to but they keep themselves very much to themselves, those hidey stripey guys), and the world's most exciting archaeological dig. I've got lots of skills and training, and probably degrees and awards, in archaeology and so I have been appointed dig leader. Some subjects that you get to study at university can be pretty difficult but archaeology is really easy. You just have to dig a big, muddy hole, find something, like a bone or an old chew, say it's probably Roman, or Neolithic, or Pet Shop, or Anglo-Saxon, or a meteorite, build a Museum of Old Muddy Things That Have Been Cleaned by Professionals, and bingo, job done.

In the Muddy Place, we discovered a hole that had been created by an errant environmentalist as a drinking spot for badgers. As spring turned into summer the water hole dried out, and the Dog with No Name said it would be fun to go digging in the hole, to see who could dig the deepest and get the muddiest. Game on. As we all dug, a few bits of old upturned stones and pottery shards later, we began to unearth the 'Discovery of All Discoveries', something so amazing that even the word 'amazing' has had to be downgraded by the people who edit dictionaries all day. Our find is 'double-amazing'. Although disputed by the Yappy Dogs, various international museums, and the park warden, our find could change people's thinking about where we've come from, where we're going, and whether we're alone in the universe. And even though a fencing repair is now in progress, and a sign in place saying, 'Keep your dog on a lead', we will return one day to the Muddy Place and continue our excavation. It's what the students of muddy history and unexplained inter-planetary travel demand. It's what the Aliens from Another World (who do, as it happens, look very much like badgers) would surely demand. Digging big holes is also a lot of fun.

## Scaling the peaks of greatness from the valley of doubt – the easy way

I always say, 'if you believe; you can achieve'. I also say, 'jumping up at people with muddy paws; never brings a round of applause'. But it's the first of those catchphrases which seems more relevant to what I'm about to tell you now. The Dog with No Name believed there was something worth digging for before he made his great woodland discovery. I believed I could headline in the Sunday legends slot at Glastonbury (and while Michael Eavis hasn't confirmed my appearance yet, I'm sure when he's stopped milking the cows and done the paperwork, it will be easily sorted). And Puppy Class Pablo believed he could lead the world's most formidable mountain rescue team. In Norfolk. Spotting an unmet need, undaunted by the distance to get there, unfazed by any mountain climbing experience, and unknowing of the landscape of eastern England, Puppy Class Pablo has overcome all the odds to establish the world's first Norfolk Broads Mountain Rescue Team (the NBMRT). Upon his return, he said the landscape didn't quite look like the pictures from my Everest expedition but it was a bit similar, give or take the absence of a snow-capped mountain range, and there were maybe a few more boats than he was expecting. But Puppy Class Pablo believed he could achieve – and he has helped make the world, and in particular, Norfolk, a safer place. Believe you can achieve, and you too will be one step closer to greatness. As I've said before, it's possible to achieve the impossible. I find it possibly impossible to think otherwise.

## If you get confused between your left and your right, lean to your left and just do what feels right

One area where I have yet to achieve greatness is in politics. I've heard there's a cat though in Number 10 (Downing Street) which makes me slightly suspicious of becoming too politically successful. However, if they let a cat become Prime Minister, they would surely prefer a dog as PM. I'm currently drawing up a political manifesto with Vegan Sydney who's good at this type of thing. She has crossed out many of the manifesto commitments on my list. It now reads: lots more bank holidays so people don't have to work and can do more dog walks, more kindness in the world, more pay for everyone whose job is genuinely useful, the creation of the NVS (the National Veterinary Service, where care is delivered free at the point of need, along with a free chew or toy), saving the planet from climate change extinction and everything to become a bit more vegan. That last point, and indeed all of those proposals, seem to be ones from Vegan Sydney. I'm not sure many of mine have made it into the manifesto. Maybe they were just a bit too great and game-changing. When you're a super visionary dog, it's hard for others to keep up with you. Anyway, soon we're going to launch the revolutionary Non-Stop Pup Party. Vegan Sydney is looking at artificial intelligence algorithms on social media to promote our cause. Puppy Class Pablo is looking at borrowing some artificial intelligence to help design a nice, colourful rosette. The Yappy Dogs are saying whatever we believe in, that is what they're against. The Day-Glo Pugs are saying whatever the Yappy Dogs believe in, that's what they're against. The Dog with No Name said we seem like a nice bunch and he'd happily vote for us.

## If you're barking at the washing on the line, you're barking up the wrong tree

Here's another tip for greatness – inspire yourself! I've seen lots of things spread around social media where someone mentions a famous quote, puts up a picture of a lake or a view out of the window or someone looking thoughtful in a meadow or something, and then writes, 'just this...' I don't need quotes from famous people to inspire me to get out of bed and seize the day. I have made my own inspirational quote posters, all from some of my own most famous quotes. Above my bed, I have the classic Bobs poster, 'Waking everyone in the house up really early gives them more time to enjoy doing stuff'. In my home office, I have more posters of some of my great quotes, 'Just when you think all the pigeons have gone, a squirrel will come along'; 'Nobody understands much, don't worry about it'; and 'Better to live like a king for one day, than have a lifetime being one of those Yappy Dogs across the road'. And there's more (and these tend to be my best-sellers), 'Think positive and positive things will happen. Even if they don't happen to you, at least they'll happen to someone else'; 'Today was yesterday's tomorrow so make tomorrow's yesterday a great day'; and of course, 'Things like success, being kind and positive thinking can all be achieved without motivational quote posters'. I always find that last one quite motivating.

## Time waits for no-one, meaning time is quite impatient, so just take your time

On some days, nothing happens. It's important to remember that. On some days you will be no nearer, nor further away from, greatness. At the end of the day, you'll be in the same place as at the start of the day. In your bed, probably. And all that is OK. It's not a steady walk up the staircase to greatness. It's not all step, step, step. Think of these as rest days. Not every day can be a Hollywood kind of day. On these going nowhere days, I'll probably invite Puppy Class Pablo round and we'll watch a series on Netflix. I might go and check on things with Vegan Sydney and see if she's up to much. I might do some admin or see what the ants are doing on the patio. I might go and sit in the garden and look at the leaves moving on the trees. I might settle down in the hallway and see if anyone walks past. If they do, I might get up and have a stretch, maybe a yawn too. It doesn't really matter. Because the next day, or maybe the day after that, big things might happen, and you've got to be ready for it.

Sometimes the solution might be closer than you think, from a source you never expected, and from an idea you never had

It was at the point that bubbles were rising to the top of the water of Part-time Lake – and we knew that one of the Day-Glo Pugs had been gone for a while – that I realised urgent help was needed. It was also when I came to the realisation that I do not always have all the answers. And this is a lesson for us all. However great you are, we can always learn from others. The other lesson is never to let a very small pug that has no natural swimming reflex enter deep water.

Vegan Sydney first spotted the watery shimmer of a reflective coat beneath the surface. Her nose and paw pointed to the spot and seconds later, brave Puppy Class Pablo had pulled the previously sinking pug from the water. He dumped the pug under the blossom tree, by the Part-time Lake (it's a magic lake which only appears occasionally in our park, but I have noticed it tends to turn up after a really heavy downpour, when it's been raining cats and dogs for a long time).

The spluttering, and still brightly illuminated, pug was OK but all of us still had the problem of getting to the other side of the park's Part-time Lake. Most of us were big enough to get across but the smaller ones, mainly the Day-Glo Pugs, were going to struggle. Part-time Lake goes from one side of the footpath to the other – if you want to get to the rest of the park, the only way is through the lake. I tried as hard as I could but I couldn't work out how to get everyone across safely. I did have the brilliant idea of using jet skis, however the lack of any nearby jet skis (mine are in Malibu, for example), was proving problematic. A second piece of bad luck came when my next inspirational idea, using a medieval catapult to launch the pugs like flaming cannon balls over Part-time Lake, came unstuck due to the lack of availability of any nearby medieval catapults. We were stuck. And for once, Bobs, the world's highest achieving dog, was struggling to find the solution.

Coming up behind us at that point was none other than Thom Yorkie, with his trademark world-weary scowl and hangdog demeanour. I normally make my excuses fast when Thom's about. Everything went a bit psychedelic last time I had too much to do with him. I find him a bit intimidating and I think basically he's from another world, another planet. But Thom strode over, and whispered in my big fluffy ears, 'build a raft from the fallen branches in Muddy Place woods, and then just float away'. The softly-spoken genius. Thom was right. Within a short while, the raft was strapped together, and I was Captain Pugwash, surrounded by my little, hi-vis pug shipmates sailing safely to the far shore.

It was the experience of needing Thom's help in the park that made me start thinking about the role of coaching in the journey to becoming great. I've been hugely successful in (most of) my many different careers. I've taken the 'un' off 'unthinkable', dreaming up many different challenges and conquering them all. And the ones that I didn't conquer probably weren't worth achieving anyway. But do I have all the answers? Maybe not.

That was when I realised I needed a coach or a mentor, or maybe a holiday. Many of my fellow global thought leaders have mentors, so I drew up a shortlist of potential candidates to mentor me and showed it to Vegan Sydney. The first lot (including Elizabeth I, Alan Turing and Van Gogh) she dismissed on the grounds that although they achieved greatness in their own way, they were dead. Back to the drawing board and my second list (including Hong Kong Phooey, anyone from the Hair Bear Bunch or brainy Velma from Scooby Doo) got rejected on the basis that she doubted whether any of them had ever been alive. Third time lucky but this list (featuring, among others, Badger Dave, Sniffy Mendoza and Mucky Gonzalez) was thrown out by Vegan Sydney, saying the problem here was that the characters only existed in my imagination. Getting a top coach or mentor was proving harder than I expected.

So, I turned the tables on Vegan Sydney, who had been decidedly fussy over my suggestions, and asked her to go through her book of contacts. We are now waiting to hear back from Nick Knowles (seems a nice bloke, good at DIY), Barack Obama (seems to know his stuff), and Jessica Ennis-Hill (good for running a 5K with in the park) before making a final decision. For the time being, I've surprised myself with a choice of stand-in coach/mentor. He's someone who is a bit weird and scruffy but thinks deeply, cares about the world, is good in a crisis and has interesting, left-field thoughts. Step forward Thom Yorkie! Thom's helping me challenge some of my established ways of thinking. And I'm helping help him with, well, bits and Bobs.

## You don't need to have a lead and collar to be a leader

The thing with a lot of self-help books, like this is, is that they often have diagrams in them. I'm aware that this book, so far, hasn't. Diagrams can make simple things look a lot cleverer. In self-help books you often see them as pyramids, with something like a foundation thing at the bottom, and something a bit visionary, a bit 'wow, that's what we want to achieve', at the top. The further you go up the pyramid, the more amazing everything is (and the more likely you are to fall off). You get other diagrams too. You get a lot of circles. You get a lot of circles that inter-connect with other circles and the bit you need to be in is in the bit that belongs to both circles. This is the sweet spot. Like the bit in a toy that does the squeaking or the leftover dessert on a plate in the dishwasher. It's the best bit.

To help you become great, and to make my book just as clever as any of the other self-help guides out there, get ready for... a diagram! My preferred diagram is a pie chart. Charts are good at displaying information and pies are great and loved by everyone and everything. The only bad pie is a magpie.

I have based my pie chart diagram on a mathematical formula I created which explains how to become great, using the knowledge of Pythagoras (a famous old pie philosopher) and Pi itself (which will help you work out the diameter of your own hot pastry products). My formula is waiting to be expertly reviewed by the dogs in the park but I'm sure they'll like it. So, what will soon become known as Bobs' Third or Fourth Universal Law of How to Become Great, is this:

BOBS' THIRD OR FOURTH UNIVERSAL LAW OF

# HOW TO BECOME GREAT...

PIE CHART

Where "x" is naturally being great, minus a bit of humble pie, times 10 per cent of being a bit magic, plus contentment with your place in the universe and faithfulness in little things, squared to the power of your ability to make tough decisions (in brackets), with the addition of knowing Tom Hanks (like I do), all over the factor of having straighter hair than a poodle but curlier hair than a spaniel, add on the quota of having good sense, common sense, and a sense of direction, include the square root of access to a park, plus dreaming the impossible while making small barky noises in your sleep, minus not knowing what conformity or calculus means, all equals je ne sais quoi and a bit of x, y and z.

Simple. And that's how you will know how far you are along the path to greatness. You too will very soon be able to make very difficult things really easy to do. It's getting easier all the time.

# FIVE

Checking where we are is where
we actually wanted to get to

The fifth step on the
footpath to greatness

## You're on mute, Puppy Class Pablo, you're on mute

How can we get to being great without being able to communicate? We can't, that's how. All the great living things communicate well. You need to be able to not only bark orders but importantly, listen, with your ears raised. How do I communicate to the people I live with that it's time for my din-dins? I don't need to tell them. I just sit in a certain spot by the kitchen door and give them my classic 'din-dins look'. And if that doesn't work, I go round the house nudging them. Message received and understood. It's din-dins time.

Increasingly nowadays we are all communicating virtually. When we can't get to the park, or when we want to link up with other thought leader dogs from further afield, we do a Microsoft Teams, or in the evenings, a Zoomies. I arranged a Zoomies meet-up the other night to begin work on my 'Big Plan to Rebuild a Tree'. As well as being a great conversationalist, I'm a keen conservationist, and I've noticed a big tree in the Muddy Place woods that is looking a bit bare. There are loads of sticks on the ground but very few left on the tree. My plan is to gather together a bunch of volunteers and rebuild the tree by reattaching all the branches and twigs. To help us with our task, Vegan Sydney had invited Double Sir Chris Packham on the call. He's a 'Double Sir' to us animals for all the things he does to promote being kind to wildlife and the planet. He's amazing. He's always talking about foxes and mice and stuff. He's like Sir David Attenborough but Sir David tends to talk about bigger animals in places that are further away and either really hot or really cold, while you'll normally find Double Sir Chris hanging around in the woods in the dark looking at vole skeletons.

Unfortunately, sources that might be close to Double Sir Chris said he would be having none of it. Apparently, he said my 'Big Plan to Rebuild a Tree' was ecologically impossible. However, from the picture I have of Double Sir Chris above my bed, next to my motivational quote posters, I know he's really into his music, and this is how I'm going to attempt to win him round. Being a great communicator, I'm thinking of this being no ordinary tree, but a punk rock tree. The first punk rock tree in the woods. A trunk of punk. What comes down, must go up, we can get those branches and sticks back on the tree.

The Dog with No Name, who annoyingly had not entered his name on registering for the Zoomies meeting, said he loved Sir Chris's #punkrockmidnight Twittering and knew he was just the sort of guy who could help us rebuild the planet, one tree at a time. Puppy Class Pablo had something to add but no-one could hear him. I think he was miming. We ended that virtual meeting with a spot of online petworking where we all went to get the people we live with and showed them off to everybody on the call. Then I passed around the virtual HobBobs biscuits, left the meeting, and started listening to the Buzzcocks, Undertones and Rezillos, as inspiration for the trunk of punk challenge ahead.

## If you can't see greatness, maybe you're looking in the wrong direction, or maybe you're stuck under the sofa

I remember the day well when we discovered the very essence of greatness. Leaves had been falling for a while, partially covering the RIP benches in the park where we had gathered together. All the team were there plus another couple of dogs I had not seen before nor since. Where had they come from? Where were they going? Where were the people with them? Why did one of them carry off that odd damp sock that I'd wanted to get? We are but passengers on a journey through life, some on leads, some on longer leads, some warming the toes of people we live with, others taking themselves off for a spot of solitude on a faraway sofa. I updated all those gathered there that day with my latest successful career move, becoming a top lawyer at the European Court of Animal Rights, and all were suitably impressed, although one of the Day-Glo Pugs turned up at the end of my announcement carrying a stick three times its size and that was deemed to be more impressive than my story.

I'm aware that not everyone has had the opportunity to travel the world and do some of the amazing things I've done, so we decided to ask the team: 'What would be great for you?' The answers were all thought-provoking, apart from the response of Stop Start Freddie who had found most of a sausage roll underneath the bench and told everyone how it would be great if he could make it magically disappear. It wasn't magic.

Puppy Class Pablo said personal greatness would be building a time machine, that worked a bit, and changing the course of history so that it was all a bit more understandable. You can't fault his vision but we did question the practicality of a time machine. Puppy Class Pablo said he had assembled some sticks and had found a watch in his house but chewed it and now it doesn't work, adding that he felt he was, 'about half-way there' with his project. The Yappy Dogs wandered past and mentioned that it would be great for them if they stopped bumping into me and my ridiculous bunch of 'believe anything chums'. Always yappy, never happy, that's them. We let them walk on by, hoping beyond hope that a strangely uncoordinated and far larger than average squirrel or two didn't fall onto them from an overhanging branch. One of the pugs mentioned it would be great if he could swim. We hoped that the Dog with No Name would say it would be great for him if he had a name known by all, but he didn't. He said he wanted to win the next Dog Agility Course Olympics, which unfortunately he can't because there isn't one. Vegan Sydney said she thought greatness was anything that people wanted it to be, as long as it made them, and others, happy. Apparently, you can help to achieve that through yoga and expensive drinks from a barista in the café. It seemed a fair point.

I've done some amazing, great things in my time, but sometimes when I see Puppy Class Pablo, sprawled on the sofa, happily enjoying the latest dog training series on TV, I wonder whether my life of reaching the highest, lowest, furthest, hottest and coldest points in the world, has been a little bit too much like hard work. Sometimes it's great just staying in and finding the warm sun spot in the house and ever so gently, quietly, falling asleep (while keeping one eye open for anyone moving about in the house and having to follow them quickly in case you're left alone).

For this self-help guide I thought it would be useful to consider your own view of greatness. I've collaborated with Vegan Sydney on the next bit, I think you might notice which bits are hers. Sometimes she's a bit astral.

So, in a dark room, with classical music playing, close your eyes tightly, open them wide, and then let your eyelids slowly fall, take some slow, nice deep breaths, and think of the darkness as a canvas. Let your mind drift and imagine. Imagine. Imagine there's a moon, a unicorn, a shooting star, a comet (if there's a difference between a shooting star and a comet, if there's not, just think of one of them), a glowing red dog, honey, a tummy tickle, a bubbling jacuzzi, a cosy blanket, waves breaking on a shoreline, someone playing a saxophone well (unlike our neighbours), smells of fresh cut grass and Bobs' jasmine dog shampoo (*for the mucky dog in your life*), and feel the feeling of realising that they might not find out about that thing that you damaged, the feeling of winning a Winnebago or a speedboat in a competition you forgot you'd entered, and the feeling, I don't know if you've experienced the next one, but the feeling of getting four of us dogs squashed into the trunk of the Hollow Tree in the park (three if one of them is Stop Start Freddie) and then running out of the tree into the wide, open space, and being able to breathe deeply again. How does that make you feel? Does it take you to a happy place? Think about what makes you happy, because what genuinely makes you happy will help to make you great. The trick, I find, is to make the connections. Join up the dots. Work out that if you can't get over the fence to reach the squirrel, maybe walk around it. If you can't walk around the fence to reach the squirrel, can you go under? If you can't go under, can you burn the fence down? Admittedly, that last option is a last resort option. They weren't pleased.

When something is going wrong,
redefine the scenario as something
about to go very right, and
see if anyone believes you

'Did this dog audition or was he a stray who walked onto the set?' was not the sort of film review of my latest blockbuster movie that I wanted to see. The critics, in every sense of the word, were none other than the Yappy Dogs, writing in *The Local News*. They were easy to ignore but other reviews in the national press less so. I mention this because I think it is important to say that we all have setbacks. Some might think I took a straightforward path to greatness, and have stayed there untroubled ever since. Well, no, sometimes tricky things have happened to me. It's how you get back up with a bit of bouncebackability that sets you apart. On a leading movie reviews website, I then read, 'Bobs' portrayal of the stunt motorcyclist was more *Evil Dead* than *Evel Knievel*,' and, 'the biggest villain in this 007 film for crimes against acting was the dog'. I was hoping for better to be honest.

But there were more setbacks to come. The opening night of my bid to establish the world's first Michelin-starred kibble restaurant led to unfavourable comments on *Bad Trip Adviser*. 'Boring' seemed to be an over-used word. Also 'too kibbley' featured a bit.

But then the biggest setback of all. The major investment in our innovative 'suncoats™' clothing range looked doomed. We'd appointed Puppy Class Pablo as head of marketing research and he had assured us we were onto a winner. In a survey of a few people who lived in his house, 100% of them in answer to the question, 'if I offered you a lot of money, and I mean a lot of money, would you consider buying a suncoat™?' said yes, they would. However, we have now found out that people don't wear coats in the summer when it's sunny. I asked Vegan Sydney to create a brand proposition for our unseasonal garment. With the help of a marker pen, adding the word 'Not' in front of 'suncoat™' she said we could market this as the world's first coat specifically designed to be used in three seasons but not summer. Genius at work again. Just like hurdlers who fall at the first hurdle and then magnificently complete the race (although way behind everyone else and never really regaining their running rhythm, so I'm not sure why they bother), we had smashed through the hurdles and will be first to the finishing line. The best way to deal with setbacks is to go bigger, better, greater.

Fresh from the impending success of our new 'Not suncoats™' range, we're already looking at even more impressive thinking. We've got a proposal to turn the local park into a global first conservation zoo, one with no cages, enclosures or crates. While we haven't as yet discussed this idea with the park warden, we have already recruited two rubbish-at-flying ducks, keen to escape the wire of the duck pond, and the Dog with No Name has offered to wear a lion costume that he has seen in the understairs cupboard at his house, to become the must-see free-roaming lion. Who knows why the lion costume is there in his house? 'Call it serendipity,' said Vegan Sydney. 'Serendipity the lion and his amazing nomadic ducks will be the major summer tourist attraction of the year,' I exclaimed. And that is how you overcome any setbacks en route to greatness.

# Even the great make mistakes, but try to make sure they're not great mistakes

'Sniffles' Flash in 'Jaws and Paws'

It's always best to hold up your paw when you've made a mistake, especially if it's a mistake that's going to get found out anyway. Being able to admit mistakes is essential if you want to achieve greatness. But when you admit a mistake, make sure everyone knows you're doing it because you have so much honesty, you're able to do it; don't let others think that you're only doing it because you're about to be found out. I admitted a mistake when I asked 'Flash' to stand in for me during the live shark scenes in *Jaws and*

*Paws*, a dog-based re-make of the original Hollywood big bitey shark film. The shark they hired was a bit gummy and would only have been able to hold me in its mouth like a handsome trophy dog. This was my chance to show how brave I was and give Flash some much-needed down time.

I also realised I'd made a mistake in thinking Sick Willow was always a really poorly dog. A long time after I'd first met Sick Willow, I did actually bump into her again. We met in the park and played chase and she's one fast whippet. I should call her Stick Willow really, as she made off with my stick, and there was no chance of catching her. Apparently the latest I'd heard is that Sick Willow is now giving Stop Start Freddie couch-to-5k-to-couch training sessions. I was wrong about Sick Willow being a weirdly sick dog but I'm right at pretty much everything else. I'm also right in thinking that to look great you have to admit mistakes, and if you haven't made any recently, just make some up. Everyone will think, 'there's someone who can bravely recognise that they're not always right' even when you are. It's win-win. Being right by pretending to be wrong. You couldn't make it up, even though you can make it up.

## If I was king for a day, I'd make myself king forever, it's that easy

What's next for me? I've a few plans. I'm not entirely sure where I've put them though. I remember one of my plans was to become a royal dog. I haven't worked out the detail much yet. The Queen of England has lots of corgis but I don't want to hang around being tripped over or mistaken for a footstool like them. I fancy being a real King Bobs and setting up a din-dins dynasty. The Dutch are really into orange which is more my colour so I could become king of the Netherlands. I think Thailand has a king, or emperor, or something. And Nepal does. It just depends what country signs me up first. I'd be really great and everyone would love me and anyone who was previously anti-monarchy would think it was lot better with a furry chap in charge. I'd make every day a national holiday and turn up to all the big sporting events for free, in the best seats. I'd have a crown and bury it and then people could have fun trying to find it. I'd marry someone I like, unlike many of the royal people seem to do. And then because I already have a home, I'd give all the palaces away, and anyone who wants to stay in them could stay there. I'd give all the royal money away and the people would really like it, and with that money, they'd buy tea towels and mugs with my picture on. Vegan Sydney says she's got a design for a chess set with me as the king and herself as the queen. Check mate.

When you look in the mirror and
don't recognise yourself, it might be
because you're not entirely
sure what you look like

It's time for some self-reflection. What have we learnt? What have we learnt and now forgotten? What did we not learn in the first place and have still forgotten? What have we remembered that was not learnt? What do we think we know that we didn't know before? This is 'Pupmaster' round two and the final round. Get a cup of tea or coffee and work your way through the following questions. If you don't know the answer to one question, just move on to the next. If you don't know the answer to any questions, just go back to the start of the book, and in addition to looking at the pictures, read some of the words. Or ask a friend.

- On your footpath to greatness, how much greater do you think you are now, than when you started on the journey?
- Was greatness what you really wanted when you set off on the journey, or was it something else, like chocolate?

- If you feel a bit greater in yourself, what are you going to do with this new feeling, and would a badge help or a new hat?
- On a scale of one to ten, how good do you feel you are at rating yourself on scales from one to ten?
- If you could reassess your goal, would you now choose an easier one?
- How would you describe your achievements, or if you haven't achieved much, can you describe something else that you're really good at describing?
- What are your options now, if you have any?
- If anything was possible, what super hero power would you have, and how would that super hero power help you in your challenge here?
- Now, imagine that you don't have that super hero power, which you don't, because you're not a super hero, what would you do? It's a bit tougher without super hero powers, isn't it?
- How will you know when you've achieved greatness, or an even higher level of greatness? Will it be when you're on holiday or when there's a full moon?
- What is still blocking your footpath to greatness? Is it a family waiting for ice creams or a gang of annoying skateboarders?
- What will happen if you don't achieve the highest level of greatness? Would you self-combust?

- How much has a cheery, confident, high-achieving dog helped you become greater than you were? Really??

## A list makes everything look more important, like you've thought about it a lot more than you actually have

Do you ever have random thoughts? Do things pop into your head that don't make much sense? Ever struggled to make the connections? Does greatness seem an elusive concept that fades like awakening from a hazy dream? Make a list and everything seems to have an order again. Lists are great for when you need a list. Here's my list of the top 10 things to remember about your journey to greatness. Doing at least one or two of these is bound to help you make very difficult things really easy to do.

1. Seize the day or maybe tomorrow – don't put off until tomorrow what you can do today unless you can't be bothered, then I'm sure tomorrow would be perfectly OK. Otherwise, if you do everything today, you won't have anything to do tomorrow and you could risk getting bored. The day after tomorrow is also OK too. I find any one of the days in the week is usually good for me. If you choose one of

the days that's not in the week then you could come unstuck. And remember, after you have seized the day, take it easy for a bit. We're in it for the long haul.

2. Walk or run around a lot, if you can – your best thoughts will come to you when you least expect them. You can't think yourself great thoughts. You have to let them appear like uninvited guests at the door with muddy paws and a bunch of flowers.

3. Surround yourself with greatness, and if you can't, surround yourself with reasonableness – I don't know about you but I always find it easier if others do things for me. I have to make sure I get enough walks, eating and sleeping in during the day. Delegation is where it's at. And not taking on any responsibilities. That's also really good. Everyone respects you more when you let others do things for themselves, and for you. You'll appear more like a leader. People will probably give you more money too if that's what you want.

4. Throw out the rule book, but remember where you threw it if you like rules – who needs rules, when there's a world out there of free-thinking, open-minded, creative radicals like us? Greatness doesn't have a rule book. There's no referee or people in shorts standing

on the touchlines with flags getting decisions wrong and other grown-up people getting really angry at them. Greatness has no defined boundary, it is hard to catch, it is elusive like when socks have been stolen and hidden under cushions, and it can get a bit hangry between mealtimes, you get the idea.

5. Contradict the contradictions – the great and the good can be both shouty and great listeners, left and right and wrong, happy and sad, visionary and short-sighted, memorable and forgetful, and kind and grumpy, depending on whether it's a good, bad or in-between day. 'Perfect' is a place in a mirage, and the signpost to that mirage points in the wrong direction, and even if you go in the right direction, someone has probably dug a big hole, meaning you either have to go a long way around the hole or fall in.

6. Don't defend the indefensible, defend the goal – you can't win the game if everyone wants to attack, and you can't win the game if everyone wants to defend. You might possibly be able to win the game if everyone wants to play midfield. Better build from the foundations up. Build your defence, get someone who does like running around a lot in midfield, and then actually get someone good up front. Greatness needs a strong base

and then something a bit 'wow' up top. The middle bit is just the bit between the two.

7. Put some cheer in your ear – don't listen to the cynics, the yappers, the miserable-ists, the defeatists, the downbeat, the moaners, and anyone who says you can't do it. Because you can. Possibly. I'm lucky with this – I have big, furry ears which help to cover the noise of those who may try to put me down. Most dogs and people you meet will of course be supportive. But there will always be some on the other side of the street, like the Yappy Dogs, barking out their negativity. Let's have a cheer for the positive people and pups. You've got this. You so have. Mostly.

8. Read the right book, and make sure it's the right way up – if you really feel you're nowhere further along the footpath to greatness as a result of reading this self-help guide to greatness, don't worry. That's my fault, not yours. Or maybe you bought the wrong book. Or maybe someone else bought you this book and it wasn't actually the one you wanted. Handily, I'm thinking of writing a self-help guide to gardening soon. Maybe that's more your thing. You could be a great gardener. I know nothing about gardening but how hard can it be? I think you just need to plant a few things, try not to eat the flowers

that you plant, not get too angry at the lawn mower, and not dig holes in the lawn. You just need to be a bit more Monty Don. Job done, a great garden.

9. Take the 'dis' off 'discombobulation' – if you do this you will become 'combobulated'. That's what I do. Who wants to be discombobulated when you can be comBOBulated? Confused? Well, if you are, put the 'dis' back on. It doesn't suit everyone.

10. Never give up the chase for the squirrel – however elusive, however much better at climbing trees than you are, however annoyingly bushy their tail, however stuffed with nuts their fat cheeks are, never give up. One day you will succeed. I haven't ever caught a squirrel but that doesn't stop me trying. One day you will achieve greatness. And even if you don't, and let's be honest here, does it really matter after all?

## Some final thoughts

Almost as fast as a whippet, almost as security-conscious as an Alsatian, almost as clever as a collie, almost as regal as a corgi, almost as good at stealing toilet rolls as a labrador, almost as good at pulling sleighs as a husky, almost as good at squeezing under small obstacles as a dachshund, almost as good at finding new lands as a newfoundland, almost as good at smelling as a bloodhound, almost as super-hero looking as a Doberman, almost as suburban cool as a shih tzu, almost as many vowels and howls as a chihuahua, almost as good at pointing as a pointer, almost as great as a great Dane but not so Danish. But I'm me. And I'm the greatest at being me. You can be second best at everything and still be the best there is.

Signed. The World's Highest Achieving Dog.
**Bobs.**

Be great to each other.

# In support of World Famous Bobs

## Jonathan Cross

Jonathan works in public relations, having started his career as a journalist. He has spent his career writing stories. This is his first book and probably the strangest thing he has ever written. Underneath his desk during the working day can normally be found a dog. A dog that has a remarkable resemblance to World Famous Bobs.

More information, visit: jcrossauthor.com

## Royston Robertson

Royston is a freelance cartoonist published in *Private Eye*, *The Spectator*, *Reader's Digest* (US and UK), *Prospect* and *New Statesman*, among many others. He has drawn for many trade publications including the *Law Society Gazette*, *Nursing Standard* and ('this week's guest publication …') *Skip Hire & Waste Magazine*.

More cartoons and news at: roystoncartoons.com